TERROR
SURFE

WRITTEN BY **JONNY ZUCKER**

ILLUSTRATED BY **PABLO GALLEGO**

Titles in Graphic Novels set

KANE STRYKER, CYBER AGENT
BY ROGER HURN & AMIT TAYAL

NIGHTMARE OF THE SCARECROWS
BY IAN MacDONALD & MARK PENMAN

THE HEAD IS DEAD!
BY TOMMY DONBAVAND & MARK PENMAN

THE COLONY
BY TOMMY DONBAVAND & KEVIN HOPGOOD

SPACE PIRATE UNICORN
BY DANNY PEARSON & PETER RICHARDSON

TERROR SWIPE
BY JONNY ZUCKER & PABLO GALLEGO

Badger Publishing Limited
Oldmedow Road,
Hardwick Industrial Estate,
King's Lynn PE30 4JJ

Badger
LEARNING

Telephone: **01438 791037**
www.badgerlearning.co.uk

2 4 6 8 10 9 7 5 3

Terror Swipe
ISBN 978-1-78147-497-6

Text © Jonny Zucker 2014
Complete work © Badger Publishing Limited 2014

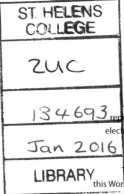
Publisher: Susan Ross
Senior Editor: Danny Pearson
Illustration: Pablo Gallego
Designer: Cathryn Gilbert

CONTENTS

CAST OF CHARACTERS

Frank Jeff Anna Gail

VOCABULARY

assembly	orb
connects	revolting
depot	stealing
ignoring	thief
machines	treasure

q

13

17

20

22

STORY FACTS

The Oyster Cards used on London's buses and trains were introduced in 2003.

There are now over 43 million Oyster Cards in use.

If you travel on London's trains and buses without an Oyster Card or a ticket you must pay a fine and can get into trouble with the police.

Some people take the computer chips out of Oyster Cards. They then put them on their watches or bracelets. When they travel by bus or train they leave their Oyster cards at home and swipe their watches or bracelets!

A team of crooks managed to make cloned Oyster Cards. They used them first on buses in the Netherlands. The cloned cards allowed them to travel for free. Then they used them to travel on buses in London. But after 24 hours these cloned cards stopped working.

In 2012, Emirates Airline opened a cable car service over the River Thames in Greenwich. You can use an Oyster Card to pay for a ride on the cable car.

QUESTIONS

1. In what way does Jeff look unusual at the start of the story?

2. What does Jeff take from Frank?

3. What connects the four people who have been caught stealing?

4. How do Frank and Gail research the watches?

5. Why are the people on the bus screaming at Jeff and Anna?

6. Where do Jeff and Anna lead Frank and Gail?

7. Why is the alien so upset when his orb is destroyed?

MEET THE AUTHOR

Jonny Zucker is an award-winning author. He has written right across the age ranges from picture books to young adult. The first book in his **Monster Swap** series with Tony Ross was a Richard and Judy Book Club choice. His other work includes the popular **Max Flash** and **Striker Boy** series.

MEET THE ILLUSTRATOR

Pablo Gallego has worked professionally in the field of illustration and graphic design since 1994.

His works have appeared in numerous magazines, as well as educational and children's books.